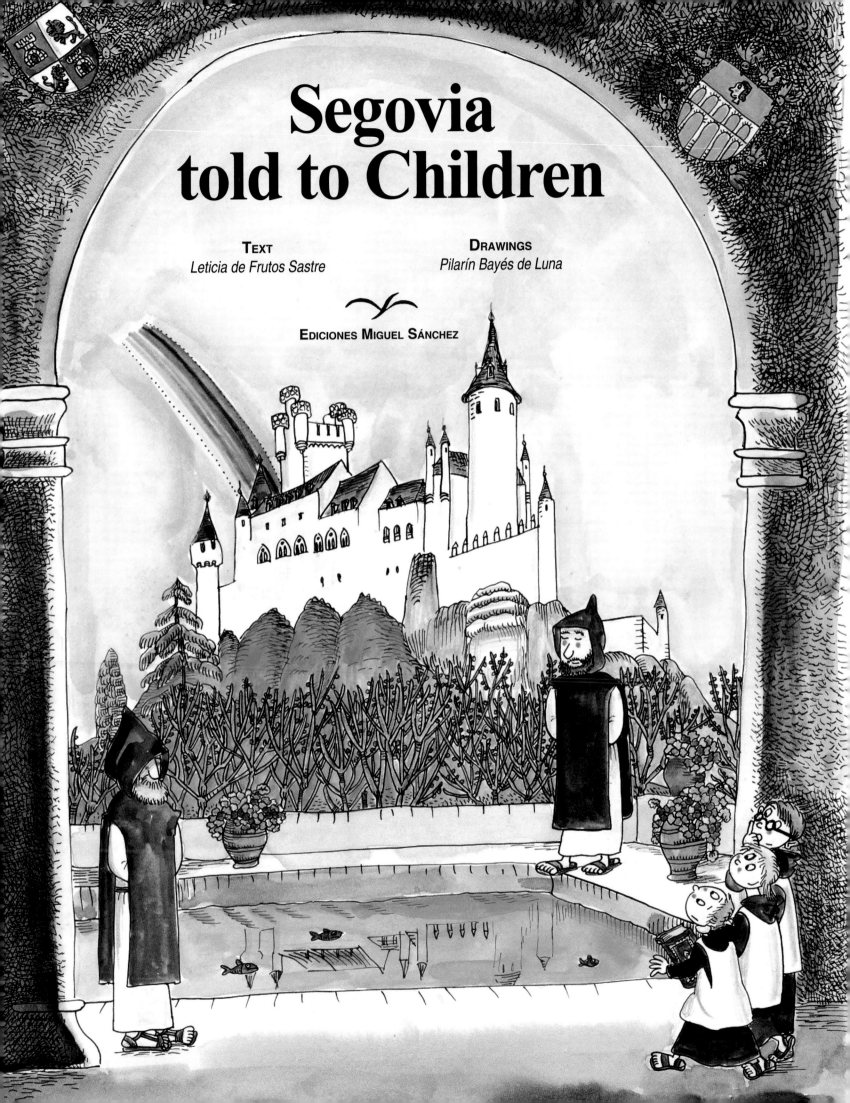

Segovia told to Children

TEXT
Leticia de Frutos Sastre

DRAWINGS
Pilarín Bayés de Luna

EDICIONES MIGUEL SÁNCHEZ

I.S.B.N.: 978-84-7169-101-9
Depósito legal: GR-703/2007

That morning, the city of Segovia was restless when it woke up. The festivities to celebrate the day of St. Peter, the city's patron saint, had taken place the night before and one of the rock bands in vogue had performed in the Azoguejo. Afterwards there had been a fireworks display. When dawn broke, the streets were littered with the aftermath of the festivities.

Eusebio got up early, as he did every day, to take his dog Peca for a walk. Although she was getting old, she loved going out when it was cool. They would go down the street Calle Real to the Aqueduct, where Eusebio would sit down to read his newspaper. Everything seemed the same as usual, except that, after the festivities, there was hardly anyone around. Peca went ahead of him. She got to the end of Calle Real and she came back barking.

'What's up, Peca? Do you want to go home already?'

Something was up… And Eusebio was even more surprised when he got closer and saw that… the Aqueduct was not there! He took off his glasses and rubbed his eyes…

'It's not possible! There's no sign of it!' He took out his mobile and called his wife.

'You'll never believe this, Maria! The Aqueduct has disappeared!'

'What are you on about? That's impossible. How could it have disappeared? Stop telling stories! That's what children do all day.'

Mario, Laura and Gonzalo were Eusebio and Maria's grandchildren. As their parents had gone out the night before, they had stayed over at their grandparents' house. They had been woken up by their grandmother's conversation and were already planning to go out.

'The Aqueduct has disappeared? Perhaps it's an enchantment, like Harry Potter's,' said Laura, who loved reading.

'Don't be stupid!' replied Mario, who was the eldest. 'That can't happen. They'll have kidnapped it so they can then ask for a ransom and sell it bit by bit.' He loved detective and police films.

Gonzalo, the youngest, on the other hand, wondered how it could have disappeared. Perhaps it wasn't feeling well and simply went away. But how?

They finished eating their breakfast cereal, they brushed their teeth, picked up their backpacks with their sandwiches and told their grandmother that they were going to look for their grandfather and Peca.

'We'll be back soon, grandma, and we'll get the bread for you.'

Maria didn't say anything to them about the Aqueduct disappearing. She thought it was the grandfather's way of capturing the children's attention. But that wasn't the case.

Eusebio and Maria lived in the square Plaza Mayor, in a small house near the old church of San Miguel, where, according to their grandfather, Queen Isabella the Catholic had been crowned.

The children liked going to see them because from their house you could walk through the prettiest

parts of Segovia. Laura was the one that knew the city best because she accompanied her grandfather and read the books he had on top of the TV set and she looked at the old photographs.

They ran down Calle Real. They went past the square Plaza de San Martín, the house called Los Picos...

They loved walking along that street because there were no cars and it was also full of shops and in the afternoons there were a lot of people.

When they reached the end, they found their grandfather looking at the gap where the Aqueduct should have been. It was true: there was nothing, NOTHING AT ALL.

'What's happened, granddad?' asked Laura.

'I have no idea children… There is no trace of our friend. But how could it disappear?'

'This is an interesting case to investigate,' said Mario excitedly.

Gonzalo, who had not stopped looking all around him, stared at the pigeons and noticed that one of them had a small cord tied around some paper.

'Look, look, a messenger pigeon!'

'A messenger pigeon? What are you talking about? There's no such thing,' said Mario, who never paid his little brother any attention.

'Yes there is, look!' Gonzalo took the piece of paper and unrolled it. It was a letter and it was signed by… the Aqueduct! This is what it said:

Dear Segovia,

I can't take any more. My stone blocks hurt more every day.

The noise and the pollution are damaging my stone and I look worse every day. That's why I'm leaving. I'll miss you lots.

The Aqueduct.

'But how did it leave? And where did it go?' Maria asked. 'We'll have to look for tracks.'

In the meantime, a lot of people had gathered in the square. Soon photographers and TV cameras arrived, but nobody understood what was going on. Gonzalo played with the pigeon, which perched on his shoulder and said to him:

'Do you want to know a secret? I know where the Aqueduct is. I can take you there. Then you can visit it, because it's very lonely.'

'Yes, yes, do tell me.'

'My friends the swallows and I took it last night to the *Mujer Muerta*.'

The *Mujer Muerta*, which means Dead Woman in English, was a mountain shaped like a woman that their grandfather had told them about. You could see it from Segovia, but it was a long way away.

'How will we get there?' asked Gonzalo.

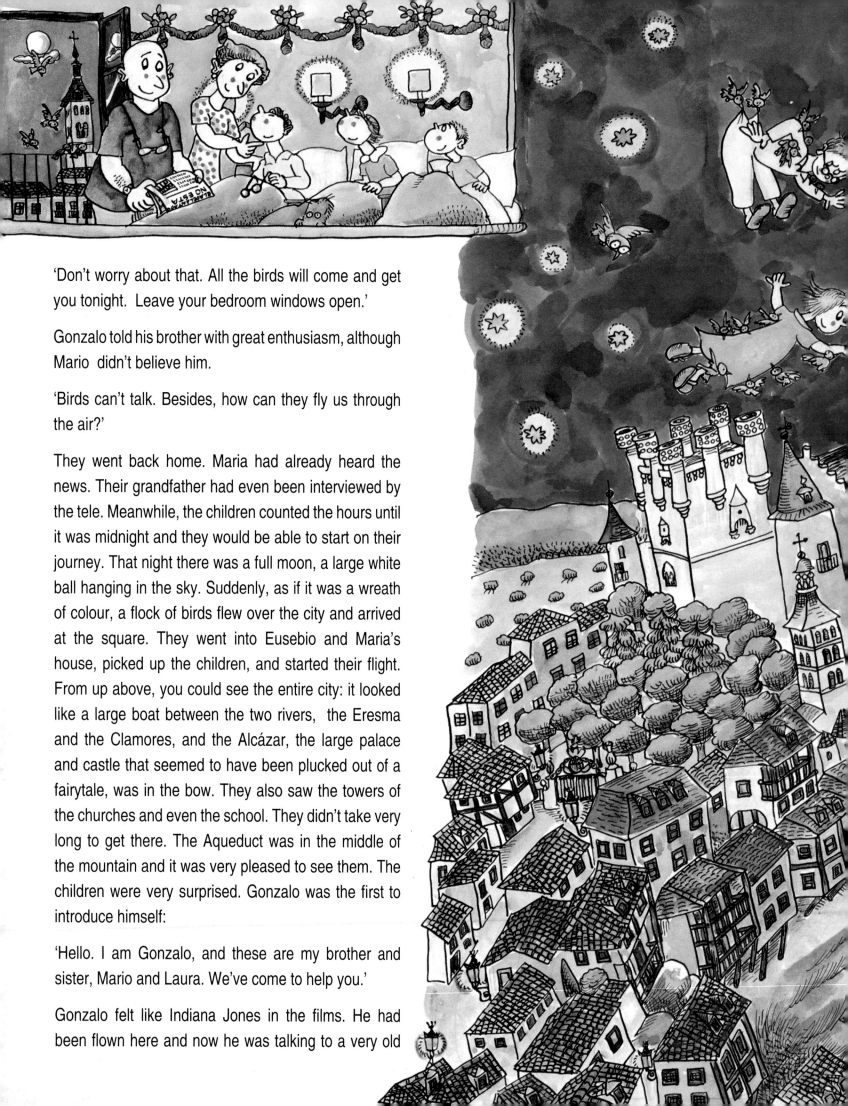

'Don't worry about that. All the birds will come and get you tonight. Leave your bedroom windows open.'

Gonzalo told his brother with great enthusiasm, although Mario didn't believe him.

'Birds can't talk. Besides, how can they fly us through the air?'

They went back home. Maria had already heard the news. Their grandfather had even been interviewed by the tele. Meanwhile, the children counted the hours until it was midnight and they would be able to start on their journey. That night there was a full moon, a large white ball hanging in the sky. Suddenly, as if it was a wreath of colour, a flock of birds flew over the city and arrived at the square. They went into Eusebio and Maria's house, picked up the children, and started their flight. From up above, you could see the entire city: it looked like a large boat between the two rivers, the Eresma and the Clamores, and the Alcázar, the large palace and castle that seemed to have been plucked out of a fairytale, was in the bow. They also saw the towers of the churches and even the school. They didn't take very long to get there. The Aqueduct was in the middle of the mountain and it was very pleased to see them. The children were very surprised. Gonzalo was the first to introduce himself:

'Hello. I am Gonzalo, and these are my brother and sister, Mario and Laura. We've come to help you.'

Gonzalo felt like Indiana Jones in the films. He had been flown here and now he was talking to a very old monument. It was amazing! The children sat down in front of the Aqueduct, which did actually look very sad.

'Why did you leave?' asked Gonzalo. 'Do you really feel that bad?'

The Aqueduct showed them one of its blocks of stone. The stone was disintegrating and the joints were getting worse and worse.

'The truth is that I've been hanging on for centuries and centuries. Life hasn't always been easy, but now that I'm so old and my health is so delicate, I feel worse.'

'Come off it. How old are you?' asked Gonzalo.

'You shouldn't ask that,' Laura said.

'Of course he can, don't worry. I'm almost 2,000 years old. I was born a long time ago.'

'Yes, with the Romans,' said Mario, who wanted to be the centre of attention in the group. 'I think it was with Julius Caesar.'

'Rubbish!' exclaimed Laura.

'Come on children, don't argue. I'll tell you my story, if you like, and that of the city of Segovia. If you knew all the things that I have seen…'

'Yes, do tell us,' said Gonzalo.

'Well, to start with, you already know that Segovia is almost in the centre of Spain, near Madrid, and it is one of the nine provinces in the region of Castile and León. It is in the north of the Central System, very close to the mountains. These lands have been inhabited since prehistory, for thousands of years, and before the Romans they were inhabited by Celtiberians. If you want to see some of the remains from that time, we can visit the Provincial Museum, in the house known as the Casa del Sol, which has just opened. When the Romans arrived, in the 2nd century BC, the city was fortified.

After some struggles, they soon conquered the city and in the 1st century AD they were even minting a Roman coin on which Segovia's name appeared. That was when they built me, at the end of that century, to take water from the Sierra de Guadarrama mountains to the city. For around 13 kilometres the pipe went underground. Then there were two huts for depositing sand, one near to where the bullring is now, and the larger one a little further on. I had a system of gates to regulate the flow and to take the water, when necessary, to the River Clamores, to empty out the water and be cleaned. Besides all this, they built my 166 arches on 120 columns, using over 20,000 granite blocks, joined without mortar, to raise the channel and cross the valley, going over the ramparts. In my first section, I only have one row of arches, but when I get to Azoguejo, the former *Zoquejo*, which means small market, where the ground is very uneven, I have two rows of arches, one on top of the other. It was very hard work.'

'And where is the stone that you are missing in the centre?'

'That is a very long story… There is a legend that says that a very long time ago there was a servant

girl who worked for a very rich man in the highest part of the city. The girl had to go and fetch fresh water from the river every morning and take it up the hills, and there were many of them, to take it home. One day, she was so fed up and tired that she promised the devil that she would give him her soul if he freed her from this difficult work.'

'And what happened? Did the devil appear?' asked Gonzalo, who was extremely interested.

'Well, yes. He was there and he told the girl that he could build an aqueduct to take the water to the door of her house. In exchange, she would have to give him her soul.

The girl agreed, but on the condition that the aqueduct was completed before dawn. They signed the pact in blood… That night a band of small devils appeared and started to build the arches. The poor girl was very scared. She didn't know what to do and so she started to pray to the Virgin Mary. There was not much left to do and the sun was beginning to rise. The devil had high hopes of winning. However, when the first ray of daylight appeared, there was still one stone left to lay.

'The one you are missing, right?' Gonzalo said.

'Exactly! And so they placed an image of the Virgin Mary to show their gratitude. But these are just legends. The truth is that I was built in Roman times. As you know, the Romans had a large empire that extended from Asia to Spain, which they called *Hispania,* and you've no idea how good they were at engineering works.'

'Yes, I have,' said Laura, 'I've seen photos of Rome and they've got coliseums, circuses, theatres… everything.'

'And what happened after the Romans?' Gonzalo asked.

'The empire collapsed. In the 5th century, the Visigoths, people who came from the North of Europe and who were Christians, arrived in Spain and they settled here. We know about their time in Segovia from the objects they left in their necropolises, which were burial sites, such as waist fasteners, fibulas, which are a kind of safety pin for clothes, necklaces, bracelets… Lots of things.

But, some time afterwards, another people arrived, this time from the south. They were the Muslims who had a very rich culture. They entered the Peninsula in 711 and they spread throughout it from Andalusia. They called the territories they conquered and where they lived *Al–Andalus.* They confronted the Visigoths, who they conquered soon afterwards. It was during the occupation that the man who was going to be their patron was born, St. Frutos, who fled with his brother and sister, Valentín and Engracia, to the banks of the River Duratón to escape the new invaders. What happened after this is that after the Muslim domination and the raids by Abderramán I in the second half of the 8th century, which was when they broke some of my arches, many Segovians fled to the north and this entire area was uninhabited, as if it was a desert.

The Castilian lands did not begin to be occupied until the 10th century, with Count Fernán González, although it was in 1088, with Alphonse VI when the city came under Christian domain forever. They erected ramparts around the highest part of the city at that time and people started to arrive from Burgos and the Rioja, Navarre and Aragon and even some French people came to repopulate the place.'

'I had no idea about the number of people that had passed through here,' Laura said.

'Well they did. In the 12th century they built very beautiful Romanesque style churches, such as the church of San Millán, which looks a lot like the cathedral of Jaca, near the Pyrenees. It has two arcades: one facing north and one facing south, with some very pretty capitals, and inside there is a nave and two aisles. Have you ever been inside?'

SAN MILLÁN

SAN CLEMENTE

'Yes, we went to a wedding there. It is beautiful and very tall.'

'Nearby, almost at my feet, is the church of San Clemente, which is smaller, with just a nave, but it has some lovely mural paintings. From where I was standing, you could also see the church of San Justo. Although it is very small, a lot of people come to see it, because it has some unique paintings at the end in the apse. There are many more, such as the church of San Esteban, The Trinity and many others that disappeared in the 19th century.'

'You know so many things! And what a lot of wonderful places we've never been to!' Laura said.

'And what happened to you when they damaged your arches?' interrupted Mario, who couldn't stop pondering about this.

'They rebuilt them when the Catholic Monarchs were on the throne.'

'Hey, they are the king and queen who were crowned in the church that is next to our grandparents' house,' said Laura.

'That's right. They crowned Isabella as Queen of Castile there. But that didn't happen in the church standing there now, but in the previous one. But wait, do you want to see what happened?'

'What?'

'Do you want to see how they crowned Isabella and what happened afterwards?'

'Can we? Can you take us?' Mario didn't believe what he was hearing.

'Of course I can. My stones contain Segovia's entire history and memory. Let me think… 1474, yes, that was it. It is stored in block II-C-4.'

Immediately a block of stone in the second row of the aqueduct lit up. A large neon sign with the letters II-C-4 in green. In a flash, the three children were right in front of it, without knowing how they got there.

'Hold on tight, children! We are going to travel to 1474. I will go with you and tell you everything.'

Suddenly, Mario, Laura and Gonzalo were in the square Plaza Mayor in Segovia dressed in 15th century clothing. There was a great commotion and all kinds of people in the crowd. Something was going to happen… Soon the music started and the future Queen Isabella the Catholic appeared. Laura, who was delighted with her dress, asked what day it was: 13 December 1474.

The Aqueduct continued telling the story:

'Isabella was the sister of Henry IV, a king who bestowed many privileges on the city of Segovia. For example, the market that is still held on Thursdays was one of the concessions the monarch gave to the Segovians. I'm sure your grandparents usually go there. Henry IV liked the city a lot. He had a royal palace built near to San Martín and a hunting palace where the convent of San Antonio el Real stands today. Do you know it? It is an impressive building! It has some beautiful Mudéjar coffered ceilings, the ones that are made with geometrical designs. And he didn't stop there.

He also had a mint built next to the church of San Sebastián for producing coins, and he founded the monastery of Parral, which is also incredible.'

'And which is in a great place for bike riding, next to the river,' Mario said.

'We can go there later if you like'.

So, with Henry IV, Segovia was a very important city, especially thanks to the wool trade. Do you know the Plaza de San Martín?'

'The square that has the statue of the man standing?'

'Yes, that is Juan Bravo. I'll tell you later who he was and what happened to him. I can see that you notice things. Let's see if you can tell me what the balconies on the houses in the square are for.'

'Hum… I don't know,' said Mario.

'For hanging out the wool to dry. Segovia was an important production centre. There were many sheep here, from the 8th century. They were the *merino* breed, the best for the quality of their wool. Noblemen and the monasteries were the owners of the migrating flocks.'

SANTA CRUZ LA REAL

ENRIQUE IV

EL PARRAL

'My what?' asked Gonzalo.

'Migrating. It means the livestock went from one place to another looking for pasture. Well, we had so much and such good wool that we exported it, and to Flanders, no less, in the north of Europe! All this trade gave the city a lot of money. They started to build textile mills and at the end of the 16th century there were 600!'

'Just think of the pretty dresses I could have ordered...' sighed Laura.

'The Segovians also worked with leather. They made shoes, hats, and everything was also sold outside the city, so Segovia became rich and prospered for centuries.

And as Segovia was so rich, the kings and queens liked coming here. It was the Catholic Monarchs, Isabella and Ferdinand who repaired the arches I told you about before. They are a little bit more pointed than the rest.

But, as you know, the Catholic Monarchs also expelled the Jews, who had been living in Segovia since the 13th century, and who had become very important. They had five synagogues, and only one is still standing today, the one that was the High Synagogue, which is now occupied by the convent of Corpus Christi. In fact, it has been a Christian church since 1410. Legend says that a miracle occurred there, which is represented in one of the canvases in the current church.'

'What happened?' asked Gonzalo.

'Well, the sacristan of the church of San Facundo gave the monstrance to the Jews, who, apparently, wanted to desecrate it by throwing it into a large pot of boiling water. However, to their surprise, the host started to fly through the air and the earth shook. Since then, to remind us of that moment, the Catorcena festival has been held for the fourteen parishes that are in the city. Actually it was a shame that the Jews left Spain because they were a very enterprising people who were very good with finances.

Many converts in Segovia, former Jews who became Christians in order to stay here, continued to live in the district called Barrionuevo, between the parishes of San Andrés and San Miguel, and there were many very important figures among them, such as Andrés Laguna, who was the doctor of Emperor Charles V and Pope Julius II.'

'Yes, there is a school called Andrés Laguna. My cousin goes there.'

'When Queen Isabella died in 1504, Ferdinand the Catholic married Germaine of Foix here.'

'There were a lot of important royal weddings!'

'And there will be many more. You see, after the Catholic Monarchs their grandson, Charles ruled in Spain as well as in Germany. He was known as Charles I of Spain and Charles V of Germany. He was a king who took part in many wars and he had an enormous empire, which his son, Philip II inherited,

who also got married here, to his fourth wife, Anna of Austria.

But, of course, an empire like that one needed to be well administrated. The problem was that when Charles I knew that he also had to reign in Spain, he brought a lot of foreigners from Flanders to administrate the State. The Castilians were not happy about this at all, so they rose up in arms against the King. One of the *Comuneros*, which means rebels, who led this revolt was the man we talked about before, Juan Bravo, whose statue is in the square Plaza de San Martín. His companions were Padilla and Maldonado.

The Emperor wanted to stop the revolution and he sent his army so that the Comuneros ended up having to take refuge in the Cathedral of Santa María, while the King's troops sheltered at the fortified palace known as the Alcázar. In the end they attacked the cathedral, which was damaged, and they seized the ringleaders.

S.XVII

FRUTOS

'What a story!' said Mario, who liked action. 'What happened to the old cathedral?'

'Do you want me to tell you its story?'

'Yes, please!'

'The old cathedral stood between the houses of the canons, who were the priests of the cathedral, and the Alcázar. It was Romanesque in style, like the church of San Millán, do you remember? And it must have looked solid and robust, but not very large. It was vaulted and it had a nave, two aisles and a crossing. It must have been almost completed in 1144, although it was not consecrated until 1228. Later

there was new construction work, including the restoration of its magnificent cloister, in 1471. But soon after that…'

'What?' Gonzalo asked, open-mouthed.

'Well, as I mentioned before, with the siege on the *Comuneros*, some parts were damaged and King Charles V, who apparently had not been very happy with the siting of the cathedral, decided to change its location and build a more modern and fashionable one. So, as the chapter also had the land that the Jews had occupied before, in the Barrionuevo district I told you about before, they decided to commission the best architect, who was called Juan Gil de Hontañón, to build a new one on this site. This architect had already built the cathedral in Salamanca, which is like ours, isn't it? Anyway, they signed the contract in 1524 and started to lay the foundations, but the architect died in 1526.

'What a pity! What did they do?'

'Luckily, his son Rodrigo was also an architect and he took charge of the project until 1529. The most difficult task was covering the nave and the aisles, but in 1542, they had already been completed. Then he finished the chevet, the chapterhouse, the bell tower and other minor work. It was opened, at last, on 15 August 1558, on the feast of the Assumption of Our Lady, which the temple was dedicated to. The best part of the entire cathedral was the bell tower, topped with a wooden spire. But in 1614, a fire destroyed it and it was changed for the one we can see now. Until then, it was so tall that it was known as the *"Lady of the Cathedrals"*.'

'Why don't we go in?' asked Laura.

'Come on then. Through the gate of St. Frutos, the patron saint of the city. Do you remember?'

'Of course we do! But, how strange the gate is. It isn't like the others,' said Laura.

'You're right. It was made of granite, in the 17th century, when Gothic architecture was no longer fashionable and the trend was rather to copy the sobriety of the monastery of San Lorenzo del Escorial. They were going to put the statues of St. Peter and St. Paul, or those of St. Frutos' brother and sister, Valentín and Engracia, on either side of the gate, but in the end, it was left like this. Close your eyes, we are going to travel to the 16th century.'

Suddenly, the children found themselves in the cathedral. It was really tall. A very delicate light was filtering through the stained glass windows. They looked up. The columns repeated a moulding right up to the vault, which then exploded, almost as if it were a soap bubble, in a star pattern. They were openings for chapels on the sides and the choir was in the centre, carved completely out of wood. Laura started taking photographs.

'What are you doing? Put your camera away,' said Mario. 'We are in the 16th century and if they see you, they're going to think you're a witch!'

'OK.'

'Look, children, the choir belonged to the old cathedral, as did the cloister.'

'But the chapels aren't the same as the ones I've seen with granddad.'

'Of course not. Many of them were decorated in the 17th and 18th centuries, as was the retable in the chancel. Close your eyes again.'

FRUTOS

GEROTEO

Suddenly, the children turned around and there was the retable, made entirely of marble, and with a beautiful Virgin Mary in the centre, dressed in silver. On the sides there were two much larger saints and it was crowned at the top with what looked like a large sun with rays, with other two saints.

'How different to the cathedral. I don't like it as much, although it seems more opulent.'

'It was made later, in the 18th century, as I mentioned earlier. But if you take a close look at the Virgin Mary, you'll see that she's not made entirely of silver. That was also an addition to the previous image, a gift from Henry IV. The saints are once again San Frutos and his brother and sister and San Geroteo.

Meanwhile, Gonzalo had stopped in front of the Chapel of San José, which was entirely Baroque.

'Look, how lovely! It looks like a theatre.'

'Come on, there are more Baroque chapels like these with gilding.'

'I like them,' said Gonzalo.

They walked in front of the chapels of San Pedro and other saints. They went out onto the street again and stopped for a moment to have an ice cream. So many things. Suddenly Mario realised that the Aqueduct hadn't finished telling them a story…

'What happened to Juan Bravo and his companions?'

'Well, that story did not have a happy ending. Their heads were chopped off…'

'Wow!'

'Charles V's son, Philip II, still liked to come to Segovia and stay in the Alcázar. In fact, he was the one that put the slate towers that are now on the top and which make it look like something out of a fairytale. If you like, we can go there.'

'OK!'

The children went down the stone street Calle Daoíz in an excited mood, and arrived at the Alcázar.

'Well, children, here we are in front of the Alcázar, which was already standing in the 12th century, as a defensive fortress, and

'Wow! Look at that great throne. I want to sit down on it!' said Gonzalo.

'Now look at this ceiling! This is the room of pineapples. It has this name because of the ceiling's decoration, which is based on golden pineapples. Or the room of kings: no less than 52 monarchs of Asturias and Castile and León are represented around the entire room.

'And which king ordered it to be done?'

'It was Philip II. Look, here he is in this portrait.'

In the meantime, Gonzalo had looked out of the window.

'What is that round building down there?'

'That's the church of Veracruz. We'll go down there next and I'll tell you its story.'

even before that, because, if you take a good look, you'll notice that it was in a perfect strategic position between two rivers. This is the bailey and here, in this wing, is the School of Artillery. In the 18th century it became one of the most important centres of science. But let's find out what happened before that. From the Middle Ages the monarchs converted it into a courtly residence and decorated it with a laceria socle painted in the Moorish style and large Romanesque windows. We can see this in the hall of the old palace, which was built by Alphonse VIII. Other monarchs that passed through here were John II, Henry IV, the Catholic Monarchs, Philip II... Let me give you some advice: keep looking up at the ceilings. They are going to really impress you!'

Look, Henry IV had the throne room built. He is the one represented in the stained glass, and the coat of arms of the Catholic Monarchs is on the throne under a velvet canopy.

'What a beautiful castle. And where did they sleep? I want to see the king and queen's bedroom!' Laura said.

'It's behind us, before you get to the room of kings. Let's go back there.'

'What a fantastic bed and curtains!'

'And look at the canopy top. It's gold! And the things hanging on the walls, which look like tapestries, are actually painted fabrics called serges.'

'Well I'm going to make some for my bedroom,' Laura said 'and I'm going to tell my grandfather to make me a canopy like that with the bedspread… I'm going to sleep like a queen!'

'Come on children, we are getting sidetracked. Let's go through the weapon room to get to the Clock Courtyard and from there I'll fly you over the Alameda, because it's a lovely landscape. That is where the Mint is that Philip II had built.'

'Where? I haven't seen it,' said Mario.

'It's that almost ruined building. Now they are trying to rebuild it. It was the first mint with a water device in Spain. It was brought from Germany. They made coins with the city's trademark. I was happy because my image was passing from hand to hand.

Here, next to it, is the Monastery of Parral, the one I told you Henry IV had built. Do you remember? And they say that the round, centrally-planned church, which Gonzalo mentioned, was founded by the Templars and that it was then passed onto the Knights Hospitaller of St. John of Jerusalem.'

'Who are the Templars?'

'Well, they were some medieval knights who defended the Christian faith with their weapons. A small part of Christ's cross was kept in this church

and on Good Friday, the Knights of the Order still have a procession with the relic from Zamarramala to the church, dressed in their capes.

And the convent of the Carmelites is also nearby. This is where the remains of St. John of the Cross, who was a great mystic and poet, are kept. And the church dedicated to the patron of the city, Our Lady of Fuencisla. This entire area, surrounded by trees and next to the river, is one of the most beautiful in the city.

'So, as you can see, Segovia has many places to discover. Unfortunately, when everything was going well in the city, the plague arrived in the 17th century and almost 4,000 people died. It was a disaster. And

Segovia was no longer a rich city. Luckily, when Philip V, the first French king of the Bourbon family arrived in the 18th century, he wanted to build a palace near to Madrid that was similar to Versailles, where he had grown up, and which was full of fountains and gardens, so he had the exceptional Palace of the Granja de San Ildefonso built. French sculptors came to make the lead fountains, which are still in use today, and Italian architects designed the palace, which is spectacular, full of paintings, statues and amazing glass lamps, which were made in the new Royal Glass Factory, which the King had built in the Palace grounds.

When Philip V died, his wife, Elizabeth Farnese, also wanted to have a palace built where she could retire as a widow and she ordered the construction of the Riofrío Palace. Now it is a hunting museum with stuffed animals, but in the park, which is a wonderful protected area, you can see live deer.

Segovia has been a very important city, although the 19th century was not very good. Some of the houses next to me were knocked down. Even some of the Romanesque churches were pulled down to make squares and gardens, following the fashion of the time. On 5 November 1884, the Royal Academy of History declared that I was a National Monument and in 1985 UNESCO named Segovia a World Heritage City.'

'Is that why so many tourists come?' asked Laura.

'Yes. Many visitors come now. Some of them have been very famous, like the poet Antonio Machado, who gave classes in the city for ten years. You can still visit the house where he lived, near the Plaza Mayor. Many tourists come. They eat suckling pig, do you like that? They take thousands of photographs and they make flattering remarks about me in languages I don't understand. But, in

spite of everything… look at the state of me. That is why I decided to leave.'

'Don't worry. We'll help you!'

'How?'

'We'll go back to Segovia and we'll convince everyone that we have to take care of you because you are a treasure for the city, as all the other monuments are. It'll all turn out OK, you'll see.'

Suddenly, the children found themselves lying in their beds. The window was open and the same moon was smiling up on high. Had it all been a dream? Gonzalo got up and searched his pocket.
There it was, the letter from the Aqueduct. It hadn't been a dream, it was true. The Aqueduct was in danger and it had chosen them to perform a very important task: help it come back to the city!

Without wasting any time, he sat down at his desk, put on the table-lamp and got out his paints. Laura and Mario soon woke up…

'What are you doing?'

DON ANTONIO MACHADO

'I'm putting our plan to help the Aqueduct into action. We have to convince everyone that it has to come back!'

He took one of the sheets off his bed and they got down to work. He got out the bag with the balloons that his grandfather had given him for his birthday and they started to blow them up.

When the morning came, everything was almost ready.

Gonzalo put his slippers on slowly and went to wake up his grandfather. The children always said that he slept with an eye open, that is why he found everything out and knew everything. When he realised there was a child in the room, he got up, put on his slippers and went with him to the kitchen in silence.

'You know where the Aqueduct is, don't you?' he said.

Gonzalo was surprised. He hadn't said anything to his grandfather. How did he know? His granddad surprised him more every day!

'And how do you know I know? I mean… who told you?'

'I guessed. I have been observing the Aqueduct for a while. I watch it talk to the birds. I knew it wasn't well. I tried to talk to it, but I see that it did not trust me. That is why it chose you and I am very proud of that. Now, tell me what has happened. We have no time to lose.'

Gonzalo told him the whole story, from the letter from the Aqueduct to the trip they had done in time through the history of Segovia and Laura showed him the photos she had taken.

'Perfect. You are a fantastic rescue team!'

Excitedly, they picked up their backpacks and started to put notes through people's doors.

They said something like this:

What would we do without the aqueduct?

Don't just sit there and do nothing.

Come and help us to bring it back.

We'll see you in the Azoguejo at five in the afternoon.

The aqua-rescuers

Mario showed him the banner they had drawn, the balloons with the messages to be dispersed through the city and the notes on coloured paper that they wanted to put into people's letterboxes. They had to gather the entire city in the Azoguejo. They had to persuade everyone that the Aqueduct needed them and that they needed it as well.

They spent the entire morning walking through the city. At five o'clock in the afternoon the Azoguejo was full…

'This isn't a joke, is it?' the most suspicious wondered.

But it wasn't. The children's grandfather had set up a kind of platform with a stand and a megaphone and he started to talk.

'We know where the Aqueduct is. It has left because its neighbours do not look after it properly, especially as it is so old. It's hard to believe. It's been here for such a long time and we didn't realise until we lost it.'

'This man is so right. Well said,' said the lady from the *churros* stand.

'What we have to do is convince it, give it reasons to come back to us. I know it is missing us too…'

There was silence in the square and suddenly loud applause startled the birds, which had also been listening carefully. In a flash, people started to get organised and to get down to work. Some swept the entire route of the Aqueduct, others put plants and flowers in the area, they even called on the Municipal Band to welcome it back. In the Mesón de Cándido restaurant they started to prepare

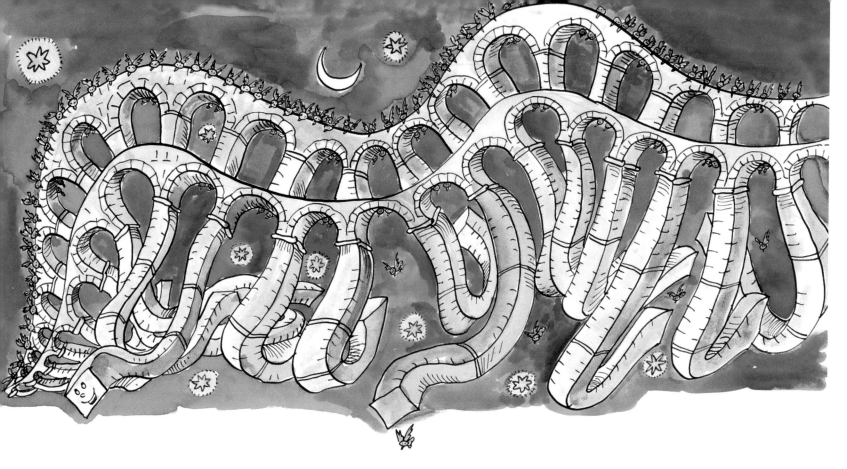

a feast with suckling pig. They even laid down a wonderful red carpet.

The children thought it was all an amazing dream, like the one they had had with the Aqueduct. Now they just had to wait for it to come back.

The evening was drawing in. Everyone had sat down in the square wearing their best clothes waiting for that special moment. Suddenly, the entire sky was covered in colour. It was as if the sun had dropped a veil of silk over the city.

It was thousands of birds. They couldn't see anything. They could only hear their wings flapping. It may have lasted several seconds, a minute, or several. Nobody could actually say later. What they saw was, like when they raise the curtain in the theatre, a marvel… the Aqueduct came into sight!

There was silence and then applause again, and hugs and music and flowers. And all the Segovians were happy they had got their treasure back.

'From now on, we will all look after you,' Gonzalo promised.

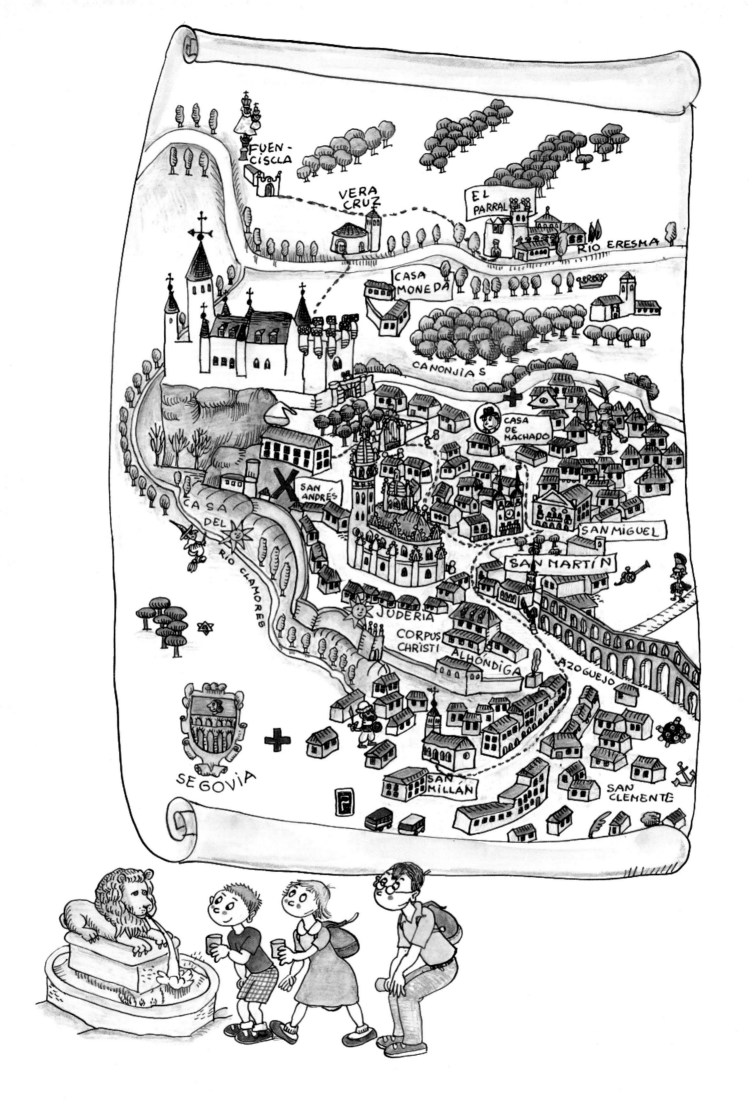

Other Books in the Series

THE ALHAMBRA TOLD TO CHILDREN
Spanish, French, English, German, Italian, Russian.

THE MOSQUE OF CÓRDOBA TOLD TO CHILDREN
Spanish, French, English, German.

THE ALCAZAR OF SEVILLE FOR TO CHILDREN
Spanish, French, English, German.

TOLEDO TOLD TO CHILDREN
Spanish, French, English.

EL MADRID DE LOS AUSTRIAS CONTADO A LOS NIÑOS
Spanish.